How to SURVIVE the SATs Writing Tests

- You've got TWO writing tests to do for the SAT.
  For each one you've got to do a different type of writing.

- There's a whole bunch of different types of writing that could
  come up. This book gives you practice for a load of them.
  The rest of them are in the other workbooks.

- The fancy flap at the back of this book has got the Rules for each
  type of writing. When you start a question, fold out the flap and read
  through the rules for the writing you're doing.

- Each question in this book gives you a writing grid for planning —
  just like the real SAT tests. We've stuck in ideas to get your brain
  working. Read our ideas and then come up with ideas of your own.

- Pick the best ideas, plan your writing and write it — then make a
  bazillion quid by selling it to Hollywood. (This last bit is optional)

Are you going to Writing Wonderland or Writing Blunderland?

Year 6 HAVE to do SATs, whether they like it or not

Writing's one of the toughest things kids have to do in the SATs.
We think they'll do better if they understand exactly what they're being asked to do.

In our **Writing Rules** book we explain how to do each type of writing that could come up in the SAT and give clear examples of how to get it right.

The **Workbooks** give kids loads of **practice** on all the types of writing covered in **Writing Rules**:

WORKBOOK 1 — FICTION WRITING

- HORROR STORIES
- ADVENTURE STORIES
- FABLES
- STORIES WITH FLASHBACKS
- FANTASY ADVENTURES
- PLAY SCRIPTS
- STORIES WITH A FAMILIAR SETTING

WORKBOOK 3 — NON-FICTION WRITING

- FACTUAL REPORTS
- LETTERS TO FRIENDS AND FAMILY
- FORMAL LETTERS
- ADVERTS, FLYERS
- DIARIES
- DISCUSSING ISSUES
- WRITING ABOUT YOUR POINT OF VIEW

THIS BOOK
WORKBOOK 2 — FICTION WRITING

- STORIES THAT RAISE ISSUES
- MYSTERY STORIES
- CONVERSATIONS
- HISTORICAL STORIES
- SCIENCE FICTION STORIES
- HUMOROUS STORIES
- STORIES WITH A DILEMMA
- STORIES WITH A TWIST

WORKBOOK 4 — NON-FICTION WRITING

- WRITING AN ARGUMENT
- RECOUNTING EVENTS
- ARTICLES
- BIOGRAPHIES
- NEWSLETTERS
- INSTRUCTIONS
- DESCRIPTIONS
- EXPLANATIONS

Here's how it works...

1) Make sure the whole class knows that:
   - the point of this book is to GET INTO WRITING WONDERLAND and stay in.
   - you stay in Wonderland by <u>meeting targets</u>.

2) Use the 'Writing Rules' book to go over the style of writing you want to cover.

3) Read through the question. Get the kids to use the boxes on the left-hand page to generate ideas, then plan their work using the writing frame on the right.

4) Set the kids targets for writing up their answers. You can base them on the rules printed on the folding page at the back of this book. We've left a space where you can write the target at the bottom of each right-hand page.

5) If a child meets their target, they're in Writing Wonderland, but if they miss one they go to Writing Blunderland — until next time they meet their targets.

6) You could circle the Wonderland or Blunderland picture at the top of each page to show whether they've met their targets.

7) Even better, make a massive poster, with stickers for the kids' names. Stick the names in Wonderland or Blunderland in a weekly ceremony. Give prizes for going to Wonderland and punishments for going to Blunderland — maybe trimming all the grass at the local park with nose-hair trimmers, or, more realistically, doing the page again for homework...

Section 1 — Stories That Raise Issues

Stories That Raise Issues — 1

Here's a very serious issue — it's time for you to have a go at writing an issue-raising story.

Hannah is upset. Bullies at her primary school are making her life a misery and she doesn't know why they are doing it.

Write a story about this from Hannah's point of view.

You will need to decide:

- How old Hannah is
- Who is bullying her and why
- Who Hannah feels she can ask for help
- How the problem is solved

Write some extra ideas for a story that raises an issue in the boxes below.
The issue in this story is bullying, so base your ideas round this.

POSSIBLE BULLIES

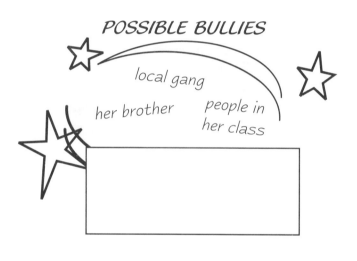

local gang

her brother

people in her class

REASONS THEY MIGHT BULLY HANNAH

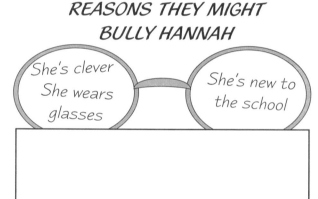

She's clever
She wears glasses

She's new to the school

OTHER CHARACTERS

her mum

teacher

friendly shopkeeper

pet dog

HOW THE PROBLEM IS SOLVED

Hannah confronts the bullies

She gets her pet dog to scare them off

The bullies realise they are wrong and stop

Stories That Raise Issues — 1

Use your favourite ideas from the last page to fill in the writing frame below.

Who is bullying Hannah and **why**?

How are they bullying her?

Who does Hannah **tell**?

How is the problem **solved**?

---

*Rules for writing interesting **issue-raising stories** are on the flap at the back.*
Read the rules — then use your plan to write a thought-provoking story.

Get ☐ *rules right in your story for a free pass to Writing Wonderland.*

Stories That Raise Issues — 2

Remember... issue-raising stories should be about things that lots of people know about.

Mick's parents have recently divorced. Mick feels like he is caught up in the middle, and he doesn't know whether to live with his mum or his dad. Mick runs away because he's so confused.

Write a story about this from Mick's point of view.

You will need to decide:

• How old Mick is

• Why Mick's parents divorced

• What happens when Mick runs away

• How the problem is solved

Write your extra ideas for the story in the boxes below.

WHERE MICK GOES WHEN HE RUNS AWAY

to stay with a friend   Manchester   a relative's house

WHAT HAPPENS WHILE MICK IS AWAY

gets into trouble with the police   meets someone who helps him decide who to live with   gets lost

HOW MICK'S PARENTS FIND HIM AGAIN

They hire a private detective   Mick comes back after a while   Mick phones one of them

Stories That Raise Issues — 2

Now your brain's bubbling with ideas you're all ready to write a plan.

Why did Mick's parents get divorced?

How does Mick **feel** about the divorce?

Where does Mick run away to?

What happens when Mick runs away?

How is the problem sorted out?

Stories That Raise Issues — 3

Pearl of Wisdom #317: Issue-raising stories work really well if
you write them from the main character's point of view.

Gillian's parents have just had a baby girl. Gillian is jealous because she's not getting as much attention as she used to. She has started behaving very badly and keeps getting herself into trouble.

Write a story about this from Gillian's point of view.

You need to think about:

• How Gillian feels when the baby is around

• How Gillian's parents treat the new baby

• What Gillian does to get herself into trouble

• How the problem is sorted out

Stick your extra ideas down here. Try and make them quite
realistic — think about what would <u>really</u> happen.

WHAT GILLIAN DOES WHEN SHE BEHAVES BADLY

says rude things to her parents

blames accidents on the baby

bakes a cake using her mum's make-up

HOW GILLIAN'S PARENTS TREAT GILLIAN

ask her to help look after the baby

ignore her sometimes

tell her to be more mature

WHAT GILLIAN DECIDES TO DO

buy a drum kit to annoy everyone

start acting more maturely

Stories That Raise Issues — 3

Set your issue-raising story in a familiar place — they usually have very normal settings.

How does Gillian **feel** about the new baby?

What does Gillian **do** to get herself into trouble?

How do her **parents** act...

...towards **Gillian**?

...towards the **baby**?

How is the problem **solved**?

*Rules for writing interesting **issue-raising stories** are on the flap at the back. Read the rules — then use your plan to write a thought-provoking story.*

Get ☐ rules right in your story for a free pass to Writing Wonderland.

Section 2 — Mystery Stories

Mystery Stories — 1

Have a go at writing a mystery story — ooh, the suspense is killing me.

As Jimmy turned the corner and began walking towards his house, the sight that greeted him stopped him in his tracks. He could see broken glass and lots of blood…

Finish this mystery story. You don't need to re-write the first two sentences.

You will need to decide:

• The ending first, so you can plan how to build suspense

• What clues to use to build the suspense

• Whether to add a twist at the end

Write your extra ideas for a mystery story in the boxes.
Think about how to keep the readers biting their nails with suspense.

POSSIBLE CLUES

scrap of red T-shirt

drugged guard dog

bloody fingerprints

car is stolen

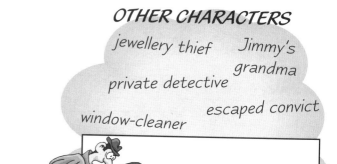

OTHER CHARACTERS

jewellery thief   Jimmy's grandma

private detective

escaped convict

window-cleaner

WHAT HAS HAPPENED?

Jimmy's mum is taken hostage

A murderer is hiding out at the house

A window-cleaner fell through a window

HOW THE STORY ENDS

Jimmy's mum (black belt in karate) beats up the criminal

The police surround the house

Jimmy catches the thief

Mystery Stories — 1

Which ideas are you going to fill in this writing frame with? Hmmm... It's a mystery.

What does Jimmy **think** has happened?

What clues are there to make him think this?

Is there a **twist** at the end? **What** is it?

---

*Rules for writing magnificent **mystery stories** are on the flap at the back.*
Read the rules — then use your plan to write a story that keeps you guessing.

Get [ ] *rules right in your story for a free pass to Writing Wonderland.*

Mystery Stories — 2

Mystery stories should be full of suspense —
keep your readers guessing all the way through.

Last night, Gordon heard strange noises coming from the abandoned theme park. This morning all of his Uncle Clive's garden gnomes were missing. Gordon and Clive have decided to explore the theme park. Outside the animal enclosure they find bits of broken gnome. They're about to go in...

Write the story of what Gordon and Clive found
when they went inside the animal enclosure.

You will need to decide:

• What Gordon and Clive think is happening

• What clues to use to build suspense

• What has really happened and how to reveal this at the end

Warm up your brain cells and write your own ideas for the story here.

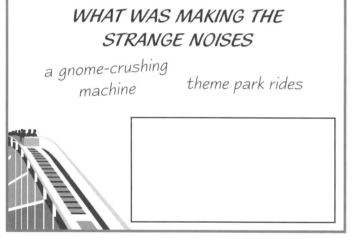

WHAT WAS MAKING THE STRANGE NOISES

a gnome-crushing machine

theme park rides

WHY THE GNOMES WERE STOLEN

to feed a gnome-eating monster

to sell to gnome collectors

to annoy Clive

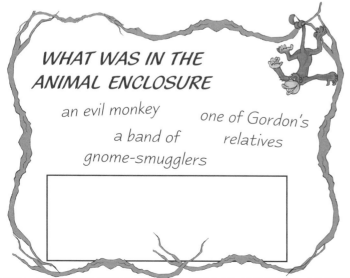

WHAT WAS IN THE ANIMAL ENCLOSURE

an evil monkey

one of Gordon's relatives

a band of gnome-smugglers

JUICY DESCRIBING WORDS

shadowy

heart pounding

crunching

Mystery Stories — 2

Now you've got a load of great ideas, you can use them to write your final plan.

What clues do Gordon and Clive see in the animal enclosure?

What do Gordon and Clive **think** they are going to find?

What do Gordon and Clive **really find**?

How does the story **end**?

*Rules for writing magnificent **mystery stories** are on the flap at the back.*
Read the rules — then use your plan to write a story that keeps you guessing.

Get ☐ *rules right in your story for a free pass to Writing Wonderland.*

Mystery Stories — 3

Here's another mystery story. Give your readers goose-pimples and shivers up their spines.

Count Heinz has invited lots of people to his castle because he wants to make a big announcement. Harif is there with his family. Just before Count Heinz is due to make the announcement, he goes missing. Harif decides to search for the Count, with the help of his sniffer dog Bruno.

Write the story of how Harif found Count Heinz.

You will need to decide:

• What Count Heinz's announcement was going to be

• Who else is in the castle

• Why Count Heinz disappeared

• What happened after Harif found Count Heinz

Hmm... creepy. Stick your ideas for what could happen in here.

CLUES THAT HELP HARIF FIND THE COUNT

smells that Bruno sniffed out

the Count's hat stuck up a tree

WHERE HARIF FOUND COUNT HEINZ

in the dungeon

in a pond in the garden

in a hot air balloon

WHY COUNT HEINZ DISAPPEARED

he was kidnapped

he got lost   he was shy

WHO MADE THE COUNT DISAPPEAR

Count Heinz's butler

Bruno the dog

Count Heinz himself

Mystery Stories — 3

Use your best ideas to plan your story here. Make sure there's lots of suspense so that readers feel like they <u>have</u> to finish the story.

Who are the other guests at Count Heinz's castle?

What was the Count's announcement going to be?

What does Harif **suspect** has happened to Count Heinz?

What has **really** happened to the Count?

How does Harif find the Count?

How does the story **end**?

*Rules for writing magnificent **mystery stories** are on the flap at the back. Read the rules — then use your plan to write a story that keeps you guessing.*

Get ☐ rules right in your story for a free pass to Writing Wonderland.

Section 3 — Conversations

Conversations — 1

So I turned round and said, "Well, now it's your turn to write a great conversation story..."

As the day drew on, the fog came down. It got thicker, until Sam and Navinder could barely see their hands in front of their faces. They were lost in the park!

"I can hardly see my hands, Sam." said Navinder nervously.

"Where are you Navinder?" replied Sam, "You sound miles away."

"I thought I was by your side! Oh no! We're lost!" shrieked Navinder.

Finish the story, using conversations between the characters to help you.

You need to decide:

• What the characters decide to do   • How they get out of the situation

Write your ideas for a story with a conversation in the boxes below.
Try and make the conversation the main part of your story.

HOW THE CHARACTERS FEEL

excited   confident
argumentative
scared
alarmed

WHAT THEY TALK ABOUT

finding each other
calming each other down
discussing what to do

WORDS TO USE INSTEAD OF 'SAID'

cried   sobbed
screamed   bellowed
shouted   moaned

HOW THEY SOLVE THE PROBLEM

They follow the smell of a bakery
They are rescued by the park keeper
They stand still until the fog clears

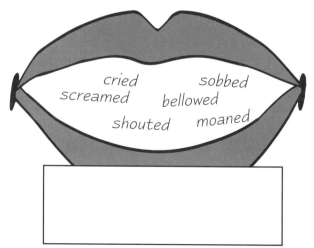

Conversations — 1

Use your favourite ideas from over the page to fill in the writing frame below.

How do Sam and Navinder **find** each other?

How do Sam and Navinder **get out** of the park?

How does the story **end**?

*Rules for writing cracking **conversations** are on the flap at the back.*
Read the rules — then use your plan to write a page-turning conversation.

Get ☐ *rules right in your conversation for a free pass to Writing Wonderland.*

Conversations — 2

Remember, 'said' is the most boring word in the world... well, after 'homework' and 'broccoli'...

Denise and Harry crouched under the stage. They had to keep their voices down to avoid being heard by the people above them.

"What should we do, Denise?" said Harry with a trembling voice.

"If we admit we've been here all along, we'll get in trouble," replied Denise.

"We'll have to sneak out as quietly as we can."

Finish the story. Include some conversations between the characters.

You need to decide:

• How the characters make their escape plan

• What problems they have with following their plan

• How they finally escape

Scribble your ideas down here. Think extra hard about better words to use than 'said'.

WHO THE PEOPLE ON THE STAGE ARE

members of a secret society

actors rehearsing a play   gangsters

DENISE AND HARRY'S PLAN

climb through ventilation ducts

go onto the stage

dig a secret tunnel

WORDS TO USE INSTEAD OF 'SAID'

whispered

grumbled   muttered

hollered

THE TROUBLE THAT DENISE AND HARRY GET INTO

captured and tied up

chased out of the building

forced to star in a play

Conversations — 2

Plan your story here. Don't forget Denise and Harry need to do lots of talking so you can show how good you are at writing conversations.

Why are Denise and Harry hiding under the stage?

Who is on the stage?

What ideas do Denise and Harry have about how to escape?

What problems do Denise and Harry have when they are trying to escape?

How does the story **end**?

*Rules for writing cracking **conversations** are on the flap at the back.*
Read the rules — then use your plan to write a page-turning conversation.

Get ☐ *rules right in your conversation for a free pass to Writing Wonderland.*

Conversations — 3

One more bit of conversation writing...

As the sun went down, Hanif and Jen had to admit that the boat probably wasn't coming back. There was no telling how long they'd be stuck on this tiny island in the middle of the sea.

"Do you have any bright ideas?" asked Hanif.

"Hmm. Fetch me some vines, a couple of logs and one of those pigs," replied Jen confidently.

Finish the story, using conversations between the characters to help you.

You need to decide:

• Why Hanif and Jen are on the island   • What Jen's plan is

• How Hanif and Jen escape from the island

Don't forget to use speech marks when people are talking.

HOW HANIF AND JEN ENDED UP ON THE ISLAND

A badly-planned school trip

They got thrown off a luxury cruise

WHAT ELSE IS ON THE ISLAND

Man-eating chickens

A fast-food restaurant

WHAT JEN NEEDS THE VINES, LOGS AND PIG FOR

A tent with a guard-pig

A pig-powered motorboat

A raft, and the pig for dinner

Conversations — 3

Now you've got loads of ideas, it's time to write your final plan.

Why are Hanif and Jen on the island?

What do they find on the island?

How do they try to escape?

What happens at the **end** of the story?

*Rules for writing cracking **conversations** are on the flap at the back.*
Read the rules — then use your plan to write a page-turning conversation.

Get ☐ *rules right in your conversation for a free pass to Writing Wonderland.*

Historical Stories — 1

Prepare to go back in time — and write a totally believable historical story.

Berlin. March 9th, 1943. World War Two.

Sergeant Wright and B company find themselves deep behind enemy lines. Their mission is to free the concentration camp and capture Herr Hamler, the Nazi general.

Tell the story of B Company's mission, using as many facts as possible.

You need to decide:

- How the soldiers are feeling

- What happens when the soldiers attack

- What facts to use to make the story interesting and realistic

Write your ideas and facts for a historical story in the boxes below.
Try and make the story exciting, and stick in facts to make it seem realistic too.

WORDS TO DESCRIBE HOW THE SOLDIERS FEEL

sick   jumpy

nervous   tense

tired   focused

OTHER CHARACTERS

British soldiers

concentration camp prisoners   local villagers

German soldiers

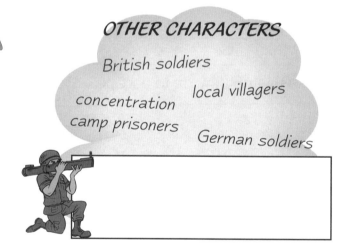

TYPES OF FACT TO USE

names of people

what soldiers wore

how soldiers lived

weapons

place names

THINGS THAT COULD HAPPEN

Herr Hamler escapes

the prisoners break free and help fight

the camp is set on fire

the Germans fight hard and the British have to escape

Historical Stories — 1

Now fill in the writing frame — use your best facts and ideas from over the page.

Who are the main characters?

How do the soldiers **feel** before attacking?

What happens to add **action** to your story?

What facts about **World War 2** will you include?

How does the story **end**?

Historical Stories — 2

You've got to know your facts for this one... it's another historical story.

The story is set in London, 1831. Jack is 8 years old. He works in a cotton mill, repairing broken threads under the machines.

Write the story of a day in Jack's life. Use as many facts as you can about life for a child in a Victorian cotton mill.

You will need to decide:

• How Jack feels   • What the mill is like   • What happens to Jack

• What facts you can include in your story to make it realistic

Write down your ideas for the story in the boxes below. Try and imagine that you are Jack.

WORDS TO DESCRIBE THE MILL

deafening   uncaring

dirty

terrifying

WORDS TO DESCRIBE HOW JACK FEELS

scared   tired

cold

miserable

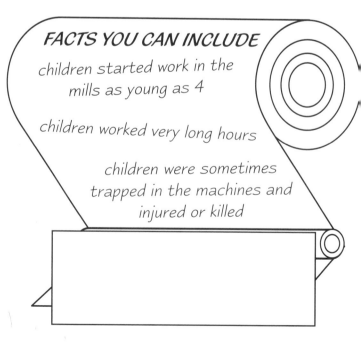

FACTS YOU CAN INCLUDE

children started work in the mills as young as 4

children worked very long hours

children were sometimes trapped in the machines and injured or killed

Historical Stories — 2

Plan your story here. Try and make it interesting as well as using lots of facts.

What **facts** about Victorian cotton mills will you use in your story?

Who are your **main characters**?

How does Jack **feel**?

What happens to Jack to make the story exciting?

*Rules for writing heavenly **historical stories** are on the flap at the back.*
Read the rules — then use your plan to write a story that's crammed full of facts.

Get ☐ rules right in your story for a free pass to Writing Wonderland.

Section 5 — Science Fiction Stories

Science Fiction Stories — 1

Have a go at writing a science fiction story — the more bizarre the better.

The year is 2134 and the Intergalactic Space Police are on the trail of a master criminal, who has stolen the Life Diamond (the diamond at the centre of the earth's core that controls the planet's temperature).

Write a science fiction adventure based on this idea.

You will need to decide:

- Who goes on the quest for the diamond
- What fantasy gadgets they have
- What problems they face
- How the quest ends

Write your ideas for an original, thrilling science fiction story in the boxes below.
Go mad with your ideas — make them as weird and wonderful as possible.

WHERE THE STORY'S SET

the planet Floop
the moon
the Hungry Forest of Barfdom

CHARACTERS

The evil Blobub King
Captain Hero
Rodney the robot
Zen, the talking computer

GADGETS THEY USE

invisibility watch
morph machine
gun that freezes time
x-ray vision glasses

PROBLEMS THEY FACE

the computer turns out to be an enemy spy
chased by giant ants
the Hungry Forest tries to eat them
attacked by a robot army

Science Fiction Stories — 1

Beam up your favourite ideas from over the page to plan your science fiction story.

What characters are in your story?

What problems do they meet on the way?

What gadgets do they have?

How does the story **end**?

*Rules for writing stupendous **science-fiction stories** are on the flap at the back.*
Read the rules — then use your plan to write a story full of crazy gadgets and geezers.

Get ☐ *rules right in your story for a free pass to Writing Wonderland.*

Science Fiction Stories — 2

Try writing another science fiction story — remember that most are based around quests.

On a faraway planet, an evil ruler controls the people as slaves. But two people plan to break out of the system, free all the slaves on the planet and turn the planet into a paradise.

Write a science fiction adventure based on this idea.

You will need to decide:

• Who the two people are

• How they break out of the slave system

• Any problems they face in their quest

• How the quest ends

Put your ideas in the boxes below
— it's science fiction, so they can be as weird as you like.

CHARACTERS

the Jambons, who rule the planet

Ying and Yang, the invisible twins

PROBLEMS THEY FACE

mind-sucking vacuum cleaner

time-travelling bat

infra-red security beams

GADGETS THEY USE

a robot seagull

a pen that fires nets out of the end

anti-mind-control sweets

Science Fiction Stories — 2

Here's the writing frame — choose your best ideas and fill it in.

Describe the planet where your story is set.

What characters are in your story?

How do the two main characters break out of the slave system?

What problems do the two people face?

What happens at the **end** of the story?

*Rules for writing stupendous **science-fiction stories** are on the flap at the back.*
Read the rules — then use your plan to write a story full of crazy gadgets and geezers.

Get ☐ rules right in your story for a free pass to Writing Wonderland.

Science Fiction Stories — 3

More sci-fi — it's the last one, so let your imagination run wild.

Some astronauts are sent out to search the universe for signs of life. They find a planet of aliens called the Hanhh. The astronauts offend the aliens by saying "hello" (a swear-word in Hanhh language). The Hanhh declare war on Earth and attack the astronauts.

Write a science fiction adventure based on this idea.

You will need to decide:

• Who the astronauts are

• What the Hanhh are like

• What happens when the astronauts are attacked

• What happens to planet Earth

Write your ideas for the story in the boxes below.
There are no limits in sci-fi, so be as crazy as you want.

CHARACTERS

Dangerous Dave
the space pirate

Lord Unghh of
Hanhh

WHAT ARE THE HANHH LIKE?

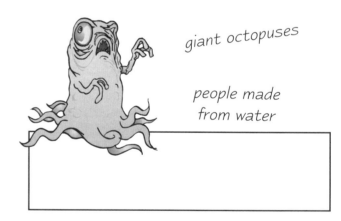

giant octopuses

people made
from water

PROBLEMS THE ASTRONAUTS FACE

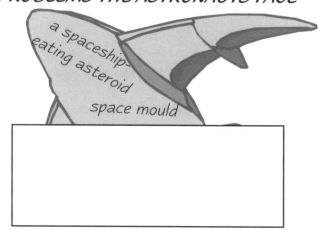

a spaceship-
eating asteroid

space mould

HOW THE EARTH DEFENDS ITSELF

makes a bubblegum
bubble around the planet

fires anti-alien rays
at the Hanhh

Science Fiction Stories — 3

Choose your best ideas from over the page to help you fill in the writing frame below.

What are the Hanhh like?

What happens when the astronauts are attacked?

What happens when the Hanhh reach Earth?

How does the story end?

*Rules for writing stupendous **science-fiction stories** are on the flap at the back.*
Read the rules — then use your plan to write a story full of crazy gadgets and geezers.

Get ☐ *rules right in your story for a free pass to Writing Wonderland.*

Humorous Stories — 1

You're going to laugh your head off at this — it's your turn to write a humorous story.

"What time do you call this and where have you been?" screamed Tom's mum as he scuttled through the door with a fish in one hand and a party hat on his head.

"Well, it all started when I bumped into Barry on my way to the chip shop to buy tea…"

Finish off Tom's explanation of what happened.

You will need to decide:

• Who Barry is, what he looks like and why he is so funny

• Why Tom is so late

• Other characters who are involved

Write your ideas for a funny story in the boxes below.
Think of descriptions and events that will have the readers rolling about in stitches.

WORDS TO DESCRIBE BARRY

chubby
mischievous
insane
scatterbrained

OTHER CHARACTERS

deaf old man
3-legged cat
angry fishermen

FUNNY EVENTS

chased by a 3-legged cat
interrupted a wedding
got mistaken for someone famous

REASONS WHY TOM'S LATE

He had to hide from angry fishermen
He entered a fishing competition
He got locked in a fish factory

Humorous Stories — 1

Here's the writing frame that you fill in — use your best ideas from over the page.

What does **Barry** look like, and what funny things does he like to do?

Why is Tom so **late** back home?

Who else is in the story?

How did Tom end up with a **fish** and a **party hat**?

*Rules for writing hilarious **humorous stories** are on the flap at the back.*
Read the rules — then use your plan to write a story that'll have readers in stitches.
Get ☐ rules right in your story for a free pass to Writing Wonderland.

Humorous Stories — 2

Make this story so funny that the rest of your class laugh their heads off. Go on. I dare you.

Gemma was at the bus stop on a wet November day, when an old man in a tutu, with a ferret on his shoulder, sat down next to her. Just then, the bus pulled up and Gemma and the old man got on. That was when things started to get a bit silly.

Write a story about what happened next.

You will need to decide:

- Who the old man is and what he is like
- Who Gemma is and what she is like
- What happens on the bus
- What other characters are on the bus

Write your ideas in the boxes below.
This is a humorous story so your ideas can be downright weird if you want.

WHAT IS THE OLD MAN LIKE?

talks to everyone

plays the banjo

WHAT IS GEMMA LIKE?

likes practical jokes

snooty

older than the old man

OTHER CHARACTERS

retired opera singer

grumpy bus driver

boring business man

SILLY EVENTS THAT COULD HAPPEN

somebody sits on a hotdog

ferret escapes and everyone panics

Humorous Stories — 2

A man walked into a bar and said 'ow'. Make an even funnier story using the frame below.

What do the old man, Gemma and the ferret **look like**?

old man	Gemma	ferret

Who are the other **characters** in the story?

What happens on the bus?

How does the story **end**?

*Rules for writing hilarious **humorous stories** are on the flap at the back.*
Read the rules — then use your plan to write a story that'll have readers in stitches.

Get ☐ rules right in your story for a free pass to Writing Wonderland.

Humorous Stories — 3

Give your funny bone a good rub to warm it up, then have a go at writing this story.

Gordon's granny asks him to paint the front fence and wash the car.

Gordon isn't concentrating on what she says and there's a terrible mix-up…

Write a story about the mix-up.

You will need to decide:

• What Gordon and his granny are like

• What goes wrong

• How Gordon and his granny feel about the mix-up

• How everything gets sorted out in the end

Use these ideas to trigger off some even better ones of your own.

WHAT THE MIX-UP IS

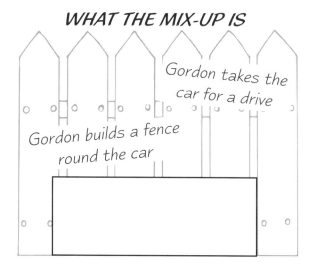

Gordon takes the car for a drive

Gordon builds a fence round the car

WORDS TO DESCRIBE THE MIX-UP

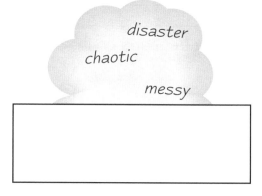

disaster

chaotic

messy

HOW DOES GORDON FEEL AFTER THE MIX-UP?

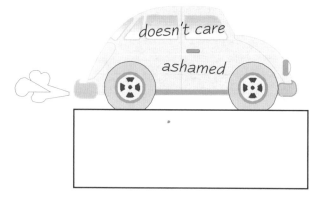

doesn't care

ashamed

HOW DOES GRANNY REACT?

she is furious

she laughs

she charges Gordon £300 for the damage

Humorous Stories — 3

Now decide what your best ideas are and use this grid to plan your story.

What is the mix-up?

What are the main characters **like**?

Gordon	Granny

How does the story **end**?

*Rules for writing hilarious **humorous stories** are on the flap at the back.*
Read the rules — then use your plan to write a story that'll have readers in stitches.

Get ☐ rules right in your story for a free pass to *Writing Wonderland*.

Stories With A Dilemma — 1

Writing about dilemmas is much more fun than having one yourself. Trust me.

Jenny and her friends face a problem. The Lard Street Gang have called them soft because they won't smoke cigarettes. Marcie, the gang leader, has dared Jenny to do it. She doesn't want to let down her friends but she doesn't want to smoke either.

Write a story about what Jenny decides to do.

You need to think about:

• How Jenny deals with the dilemma

• A good ending that makes the reader think how they would react

Write your ideas for a story about a dilemma in the boxes below.
The dilemma here is whether Jenny should accept the dare to smoke or not.

SETTINGS FOR THE DARE

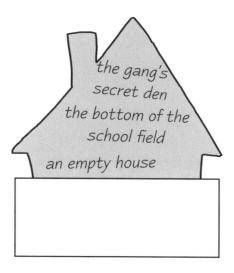

the gang's secret den

the bottom of the school field

an empty house

WORDS TO DESCRIBE JENNY'S DILEMMA

upsetting

confusing

impossible

puzzling

stressful

OTHER CHARACTERS

Jenny's best friend, Becky

Laura, Marcie's mean side-kick

Mrs Ramsbottom, a teacher

HOW THE STORY ENDS

Jenny double-dares Marcie, who doesn't dare do it

Jenny tells a teacher and Marcie gets in trouble

Jenny does the dare so the gang leaves her alone

Stories With A Dilemma — 1

Here's a little dilemma — which ideas are you going to put in the writing frame?

Where does the dare take place?	**Who** else is in the story?

What does Jenny **choose** to do?	**What** is the story **teaching** the reader?

*Rules for writing delectable **dilemma stories** are on the flap at the back.*
Read the rules — then use your plan to write a story with a head-holding dilemma.

Get ☐ rules right in your story for a free pass to Writing Wonderland.

Stories With A Dilemma — 2

Read the question and plan what your story is going to be about — what a dilemma.

Greg and Tamsin are playing tennis when the ball goes through a window and smashes it. Just then a football, kicked by their enemy Sid, flies through the broken window. Should Greg and Tamsin own up to smashing the window or blame Sid?

Write a story about what Greg and Tamsin decide to do.

You will need to decide:

• Where the story takes place

• How the children deal with the problem

• How to end the story by making the reader think about what they would do

Have a good think about all these things before you write your final plan.

HOW DO GREG AND TAMSIN FEEL WHEN THE WINDOW BREAKS?

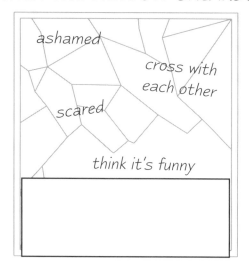

ashamed

cross with each other

scared

think it's funny

WHY DON'T GREG AND TAMSIN LIKE SID?

he's a bully

he has red hair

he once pushed Greg in the lake

PUNISHMENT FOR BREAKING THE WINDOW

being grounded

prison

have to pay for window

Stories With A Dilemma — 2

Choose the best ideas from the last page to help you plan your dilemma story.

Whose window is smashed?

How do Greg and Tamsin **react** when the window breaks?

What reasons do Greg and Tamsin have for owning up?

What reasons do Greg and Tamsin have for **not** owning up?

What do they **decide** to do in the end?

What is the **message** of the story?

*Rules for writing delectable **dilemma stories** are on the flap at the back.*
Read the rules — then use your plan to write a story with a head-holding dilemma.

Get ☐ *rules right in your story for a free pass to Writing Wonderland.*

© CGP 2003

Section 7 — Stories With A Dilemma

Stories With A Twist — 1

Come on, let's twist again — write a story with an ending you wouldn't expect.

Ben could hear a noise. It was coming from his basement. He decided to investigate.

What does Ben find in the cellar?

Tell the story of his investigation, but try to add a twist at the end.

You will need to decide:

• How to build up suspense

• What is making the noise

• What the twist in your story is

Write your ideas for a story with a twist in the boxes below.
Remember that the twist should stun the readers — they shouldn't see it coming.

WHAT BEN MIGHT HAVE HEARD

someone crying

gentle tapping

dripping water

OTHER CHARACTERS

a lost kitten

a ghost of a little girl

a burglar

the tooth fairy

WORDS TO BUILD UP SUSPENSE

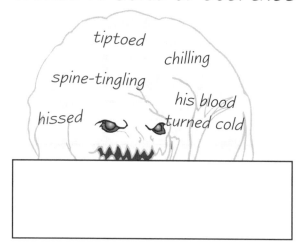

tiptoed

chilling

spine-tingling

his blood

hissed

turned cold

POSSIBLE TWISTS

it's Ben making the noise

Ben is a ghost and the little girl is real

the same sound is coming from everyone's basement

Stories With A Twist — 1

Use your favourite ideas from over the page to fill in the writing frame below.

What does Ben **think** is making the noise?

What is making the noise?

What is the **twist** at the end?

*Rules for writing stunning **stories with a twist** are on the flap at the back.*
Read the rules — then use your plan to write a story that'll totally flummox readers.

Get ☐ rules right in your story for a free pass to Writing Wonderland.

© CGP 2003

Section 8 — Stories With A Twist

Stories With A Twist — 2

Stories with twists usually feature lots of... watermelons. (You didn't see that coming did you?)

It's Claire's 10th birthday. Claire and Sharaz have been playing in the park. They get back to Claire's house to find the door open and the house deserted. There is a big muddy footprint on the kitchen floor.

Write a story based on this idea. End the story with a twist.

You will need to decide:

• What Claire and Sharaz do next

• Who or what left the footprint

• Where Claire's family has gone

• What the twist in the tale is

Write down all your ideas. Try and keep your reader guessing until the very end.

WORDS TO DESCRIBE HOW CLAIRE AND SHARAZ FEEL

frightened annoyed

anxious

WHAT THEY MIGHT THINK HAS HAPPENED TO CLAIRE'S FAMILY

They've gone somewhere fun without Claire

They've just popped out

They've been kidnapped

THINGS THAT COULD HAPPEN

They hear a noise upstairs and go to investigate

They look in different places, and one of them disappears

POSSIBLE TWISTS

It's a surprise birthday party, but they forgot about Claire

They were all kidnapped by a Bigfoot

Stories With A Twist — 2

Choose your best ideas and use them to complete the writing frame below.

What do Claire and Sharaz **think** has happened to Claire's family?

What has happened to Claire's family?

Who or **what** left the footprint?

What is the **twist**?

*Rules for writing stunning **stories with a twist** are on the flap at the back.*
Read the rules — then use your plan to write a story that'll totally flummox readers.
Get ☐ rules right in your story for a free pass to Writing Wonderland.

Stories With A Twist — 3

Stories are much more fun if the reader doesn't know what's going to happen at the end.

Bethany opened the front door and went inside. She put down her school bag, hung up her coat and went upstairs to change out of her uniform. On her bed was a folded piece of paper with her name on it. She unfolded the paper and read…

Write the story of what happens next. You can write the story in any style you like, but try to put a twist at the end.

You will need to decide:

- What is written on the piece of paper
- Who left the piece of paper for Bethany
- What happens next
- What the twist in the tale is

Use these boxes to write down you ideas for the story.
You can make the twist as wacky as you like.

POSSIBLE STORY STYLES

horror story

mystery story

fantasy adventure

THINGS THE NOTE COULD BE

a ransom note

an invitation

a treasure map   a clue

THINGS BETHANY COULD DO

follow the note's instructions

go downstairs to tell her Mum

POSSIBLE TWISTS

The note was a trap set by the three-eyed, purple-headed monster that lives in Bethany's wardrobe

Stories With A Twist — 3

Here's the final writing frame in the book — so make sure you fill it in extra well.

What is written on the
piece of paper?

Who are the main characters
in your story?

What does Bethany do after she has read the note?

What is the **twist** in your story?